CLASSICS
Illustrated ®

Mark Twain
THE PRINCE
AND
THE PAUPER

essay by
Andrew J. Hoffman Ph.D.

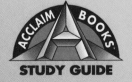

ACCLAIM BOOKS
STUDY GUIDE

The Prince and the Pauper

art by Arnold Hicks

Classics Illustrated: The Prince and the Pauper
© Twin Circle Publishing Co.,
a division of Frawley Enterprises; licensed to First Classics, Inc.
All new material and compilation © 1997 by Acclaim Books, Inc.

Dale-Chall R.L.: 8.0

ISBN 1-57840-012-0

Classics Illustrated® is a registered trademark
of the Frawley Corporation.

Acclaim Books, New York, NY
Printed in the United States

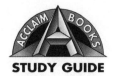

STUDY GUIDE

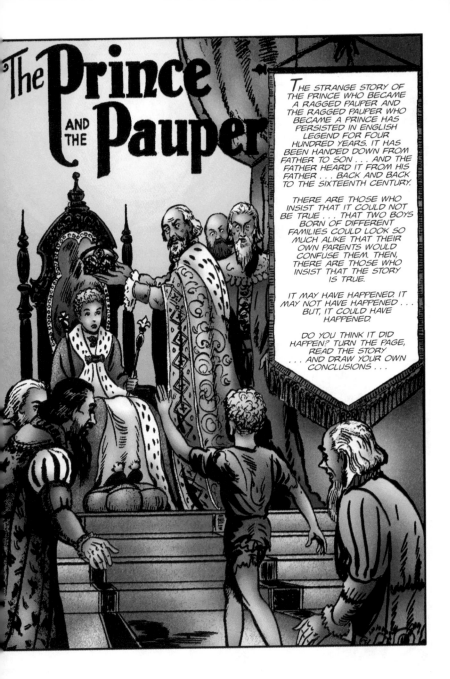

The Prince AND THE Pauper

THE STRANGE STORY OF THE PRINCE WHO BECAME A RAGGED PAUPER AND THE RAGGED PAUPER WHO BECAME A PRINCE HAS PERSISTED IN ENGLISH LEGEND FOR FOUR HUNDRED YEARS. IT HAS BEEN HANDED DOWN FROM FATHER TO SON ... AND THE FATHER HEARD IT FROM HIS FATHER ... BACK AND BACK TO THE SIXTEENTH CENTURY.

THERE ARE THOSE WHO INSIST THAT IT COULD NOT BE TRUE ... THAT TWO BOYS BORN OF DIFFERENT FAMILIES COULD LOOK SO MUCH ALIKE THAT THEIR OWN PARENTS WOULD CONFUSE THEM. THEN, THERE ARE THOSE WHO INSIST THAT THE STORY IS TRUE.

IT MAY HAVE HAPPENED. IT MAY NOT HAVE HAPPENED ... BUT, IT COULD HAVE HAPPENED.

DO YOU THINK IT DID HAPPEN? TURN THE PAGE, READ THE STORY ... AND DRAW YOUR OWN CONCLUSIONS ...

IN THE SIXTEENTH CENTURY, IN THE LONDON SLUMS, A BOY NAMED TOM CANTY WAS BORN.

THERE WAS NO HAPPINESS AT HIS COMING

A BABY! ANOTHER MOUTH TO FEED!

AND ON THAT VERY SAME DAY, ANOTHER BOY WAS BORN . . . EDWARD TUDOR. THERE WAS GREAT HAPPINESS AT HIS COMING.

THERE HE IS, SIRE. THE NEW *PRINCE OF WALES!*

ALL ENGLAND, TOO, WAS JOYFUL AT EDWARD'S BIRTH.

YEARS PASSED, AND LIFE WAS DIFFERENT FOR THE TWO BOYS. WHILE EDWARD, THE PRINCE, SPENT HIS TIME ACQUIRING THE WORLD'S KNOWLEDGE THROUGH TUTORS . . .

THIS MORNING WE'LL REVIEW THE FOLLOWING VERBS.

. . . TOM HAD BEEN MADE TO BEG . . .

WHAT . . . YOU'VE BEGGED ONLY A SINGLE PENNY TODAY! TAKE THIS, YOU LAZY FOOL!

BUT TOM, TOO HAD HIS TUTOR . . . FATHER ANDREW, A KINDLY OLD PRIEST WHO LIVED NEARBY . . .

ARE YOU **SURE** YOU KNOW TODAY'S LATIN LESSON PERFECTLY, TOM?

OH YES, FATHER ANDREW! AND NOW, PLEASE TELL ME ANOTHER STORY ABOUT PRINCES AND KINGS AND CASTLES!

THE MORE STORIES TOM HEARD, THE MORE HE DREAMED ABOUT PRINCES . . . AND KINGS . . . AND CASTLES . . .

WORRY NOT, MY LADY! I, PRINCE TOM, HAVE COME TO RESCUE YOU!

. . . AND THE MORE TOM DREAMED ABOUT PRINCES . . . THE MORE PRINCELY HE BECAME!

WHAT, KNAVE? . . . YOU DOUBT MY WORD WHEN I TELL YOU I EARNED FIVE PENCE TODAY? FROM ME?

WHAT'S GOT INTO YOU, TOM? YOU TALK SO FUNNY.

TOM'S FRIENDS WERE FIRST AMUSED, THEN AWED. TOM EVEN ORGANIZED A ROYAL COURT.

I DUB YOU FIRST LORD OF THE ROYAL FOOTWEAR. IT WOULD BE YOUR DUTY TO PUT ON MY SHOES, IF I HAD SHOES.

OH, THANK YOU, PRINCE TOM!

TOM'S DREAMS CENTERED ABOUT ONE GREAT AIM.

IF I COULD SEE A PRINCE . . . A REAL ONE IN ALL HIS FINERY! WHY, I'D BE HAPPY FOR THE REST OF MY DAYS.

ONE DAY HE WENT FOR A LONG WALK . . . PAST STREETS HE HAD NEVER SEEN BEFORE . . .

WHAT BEAUTIFUL BUILDINGS! WHY EVEN A PRINCE MIGHT LIVE HERE.

...THEN HE CAME TO THE MOST IMPRESSIVE BUILDING OF ALL ... WESTMINSTER PALACE!

AND ... AND THIS CASTLE... A PRINCE **MUST** LIVE HERE! I'M GOING TO HAVE A CLOSER LOOK!

WHY. ..WHY, THERE HE IS! THERE'S A REAL PRINCE!

SUDDENLY ...

MIND YOUR MANNERS ... YOUNG BEGGAR! AWAY FROM THE GATE!

YOU, GUARD, HOW DARE YOU TREAT THE LAD LIKE THAT! HOW DARE YOU TREAT EVEN MY FATHER'S LOWEST SUBJECT IN THAT FASHION! OPEN THE GATE FOR HIM!

AS TOM SPRAWLED THERE AMIDST THE JEERING AND LAUGHING CROWD.

YOU LOOK TIRED AND HUNGRY ... AND YOU'VE BEEN TREATED POORLY. COME WITH ME!

W-WITH YOU, SIR?

ARE YOU SURE YOU WANT ME TO COME IN WITH YOU, SIR?

OF COURSE. COME, DON'T BE NERVOUS.

WHEN TOM HEARD ABOUT COURT LIFE . . .

YOU MEAN YOU WEAR BEAUTIFUL CLOTHES LIKE THESE ALL THE TIME? OH, YOUR LIFE MUST BE WONDERFUL!

AND WHEN PRINCE EDWARD HEARD ABOUT LIFE IN THE SLUMS...

YOU MEAN YOU SWIM IN THE CANALS AND RIVERS . . . AND PLAY WITH MUD. . . AND SPLATTER EACH OTHER IN FUN? OH, YOUR LIFE MUST BE WONDERFUL!

IF I COULD DON YOUR CLOTHES AND PLAY IN THE MUD JUST ONCE, HOW HAPPY I WOULD BE!

AND IF I COULD WEAR BEAUTIFUL CLOTHES LIKE YOURS JUST ONCE . . . HOW HAPPY I WOULD BE!

WOULD YOU LIKE THAT, TOM? VERY WELL, THEN . . . SO IT SHALL BE! COME, LET US CHANGE CLOTHES!

QUICKLY THE CHANGE WAS MADE . . . AND THE PRINCE AND THE PAUPER STARED AT EACH OTHER . . .

WHAT . . . WHAT DO YOU MAKE OF THIS, TOM?

I KNOW I . . . I'M THINKING THE SAME THING YOU ARE . . . BUT IT'S NOT FOR ONE OF MY RANK TO SAY IT, SIR. *YOU* SAY IT!

YOU AND I ARE IDENTICAL, TOM . . . SAME HAIR, SAME EYES, SAME FACE, SAME FORM . . . EVEN THE SAME VOICE! ONLY OUR CLOTHES MAKE US DIFFERENT!

YOU FOOLS! TAKE THIS . . . BUT WAIT TILL TOMORROW . . . I'LL BUILD YOU A *GALLOWS!*

O-O-O-H!

THIS RAGAMUFF-IN'S GONE BEYOND FUN! GET THE DOG AND TO THE POND WITH HIM.

AND ONCE AGAIN, THE PRINCE MET SAD TREATMENT AT THE HANDS OF A CROWD.

THAT'LL TEACH YOU NOT TO KICK YOUR BETTERS!

THE PRINCE BEGAN TO WAN-DER AGAIN. HOURS PASSED AND NIGHT CAME . . . A RAW, WINDY NIGHT . . .

NO ONE BELIEVES ME! MY ONLY CHANCE IS TO FIND TOM CANTY'S HOME. HIS FAMILY WILL PROVE TO THE PALACE GUARDS THAT I AM NOT TOM!

THIS IS THE KIND OF NEIGH-BORHOOD HE DESCRIBED! I WONDER IF HE LIVES ANYWHERE NEAR HERE . . .

SUDDENLY . . .

HELP! H-E-L-P!

WHAT ARE YOU YELLING ABOUT, WRETCH . . . AND WHAT ARE YOU DOING OUT AT THIS HOUR? I'LL BREAK EVERY BONE IN YOUR BODY . . . OR MY NAME'S NOT JOHN CANTY!

JOHN CANTY! WHAT LUCK! ARE YOU REALLY *HIS* FATHER?

HIS FATHER! WHAT TALK IS THIS? I'M *YOUR* FATHER!

OH, PLEASE SIR . . . DON'T JEST WITH ME! I'M IN TERRIBLE TROUBLE! YOU MUST COME WITH ME TO THE PALACE GUARDS AND CONVINCE THEM THAT I'M THE PRINCE OF WALES!

PRINCE OF WALES! HE'S GONE *CRAZY!* COME, MADMAN . . . PERHAPS A GOOD SOUND BEATING WILL BRING BACK YOUR SANITY!

SILENCE . . . YOU MADMAN! I'LL QUIET YOU DOWN!

LET ME GO . . . I TELL YOU! I'M NOT YOUR SON! I'M THE PRINCE OF WALES!

SUDDENLY, FATHER ANDREW APPEARED AT THE HEAD OF THE CROWD . . .

STOP! DON'T HIT THE BOY! HE MEANS NO HARM . . . HE'S SICK!

ENOUGH OF THIS! YOU LAZY FOOL... HOW MUCH MONEY HAVE YOU GATHERED WITH YOUR BEGGING TODAY?

BEGGING! DON'T OFFEND ME, KNAVE! I'VE TOLD YOU THAT I'M A KING'S SON!

OFFEND YOU, EH? I'LL SHOW YOU WHOSE SON YOU ARE!

MERCILESSLY, CANTY BEAT THE PRINCE. FINALLY...

ALL RIGHT... TO BED, ALL OF YOU! THIS ENTERTAINMENT HAS TIRED ME!

TIRED AND WORN, THE PRINCE SLUMPED ON HIS BED OF STRAW AND BAGS, AND FELL ASLEEP INSTANTLY.

THERE IS SOMETHING STRANGE ABOUT TOM TONIGHT. CAN IT BE THAT HE IS NOT MY SON?

OH, NO, I MUST BE MAD MYSELF TO BELIEVE THAT! AND YET... BUT WAIT! I CAN FIND OUT AT ONCE!

TOM HAS HAD THE HABIT SINCE HE WAS A BABY, OF PUTTING HIS HAND BEFORE HIS EYES WHENEVER HE WAS STARTLED! I'LL WAKE HIM NOW, AND SEE...

U ALL HEARD!
O *QUICKLY*!
E'LL SEPARATE
ND MEET AT
E LONDON
RIDGE!

CANTY, THE PRINCE, AND THE OTHERS RUSHED OUT INTO THE STREET . . . AND SAW THAT A HUGE CELEBRATION WAS IN PROGRESS . . .

WHERE ARE YOU RUSHING, FRIEND? ARE YOU BOTHERING WITH BUSINESS WHEN MEN ARE MAKING HOLIDAY?

MY BUSINESS IS MY *OWN*! LET ME *PASS*!

H, NO, FRIEND! YOU SHALL NOT PASS TIL YOU'VE DRUNK FROM THE VING CUP! DRINK TO THE PRINCE OF WALES!

HAND IT HERE!

CANTY LIFTED THE CUP WITH BOTH HANDS, RELEASING THE HAND OF THE PRINCE.

I MAY NOT GET ANOTHER CHANCE! I'M GOING TO RUN FOR IT!

EASTING IN MY HON-
R? DON'T THEY KNOW
HAT I'M MISSING? IF
M CANTY'S SOMEHOW
OOLED THE OTHERS
INTO THINKING HE'S
ME, I'LL WRECK HIS
LANS SOON
ENOUGH!

...BUT, SIRE, HAVE YOU FORGOTTEN THE DUKE OF NORFOLK, WHO IS TO PERFORM THE CEREMONY, IS YOUR POLITICAL PRISONER? YOU HAD HIM LOCKED IN THE TOWER. HE IS TO DIE AT SUNRISE!

SO HE SHALL! A NEW GRAND MAR-SHALL WILL PER-FORM THE CEREMONY.

VERY GOOD, SIR!

SITTING IN THE PRINCE'S ROOM LATER THAT DAY, TOM FELT ALONE AND MISERABLE.

IT WAS HORRIBLE. THE KING'S ORDER. MUST THAT MAN DIE? OH, IF ONLY THE REAL PRINCE WOULD RETURN!

LATER THAT DAY, LORD HERTFORD VISITED TOM...

MAY I HAVE A WORD WITH YOU, MY PRINCE?

I'M NOT THE PRINCE ...OH NEVER MIND. WHAT IS IT YOU WISH?

YOU MUST NOT DENY THAT YOU ARE THE PRINCE.

I SUPPOSE I'LL HAVE TO DO WHAT THEY SAY.

AND SO TOM TOOK OVER THE PRINCE'S DUTIES. HE MADE MANY MISTAKES. AT DINNER HE WAS HANDED A NAPKIN...

THIS IS VERY PRETTY ... BUT I PRAY YOU TAKE IT AWAY. I MAY SOIL IT.

WHEN HE WAS HANDED A FINGER BOWL WITH ROSE WATER . . .

HE'S DRINKING FROM IT!

I DON'T LIKE IT. IT HAS A PRETTY FLAVOR . . . BUT IT LACKS STRENGTH!

THEN WHEN NUTS WERE SERVED, TOM ATE SOME . . . AND STUFFED HIS POCKETS WITH THE OTHERS!

I'LL KEEP THE REST FOR LATER.

LATER THAT AFTERNOON, KING HENRY WHO HAD BEEN ILL FOR A LONG TIME WOKE FEELING MUCH WORSE.

THE LORD CHANCELLOR WAITS OUTSIDE, SIRE.

HAVE HIM COME IN. I'M SINKING FAST!

THE LORD CHANCELLOR WAS ADMITTED . . .

THE PEERS HAVE MET AND CONFIRMED THE DUKE OF NORFOLK'S DEATH. THEY HUMBLY AWAIT YOUR FURTHER ACTION.

GOOD! I'LL ATTACH THE SEAL TO HIS DEATH WARRANT!

THE KING TRIED TO RISE . . . BUT FELL BACK WEAKLY.

I'M TOO SICK TO GET UP. YOU HAD BEST ATTEND TO THE GREAT SEAL.

SO IT SHALL BE, SIRE. BUT WHERE IS THE GREAT SEAL?

DON'T YOU REMEM-BER, SIRE . . . YOU TOOK IT FROM ME SEVERAL DAYS AGO.

THE SEAL! IT'S ALWAYS IN YOUR POS-SESSION. YOU MUST KNOW WHERE IT IS!

TRUE, HERT-FORD! I GAVE IT TO THE PRINCE FOR SAFE KEEPING! GET IT FROM HIM!

MINUTES LATER . . .

FURTHER SAD TID-INGS, MY KING. BE-CAUSE OF HIS AFFLIC-TION, THE PRINCE CANNOT REMEMBER THE SEAL AT ALL.

POOR LAD! HE IS INDEED UNWELL

VERY GOOD, SIRE!

NOTHING WILL STOP ME FROM SEEING THE TRAITOR DEAD BY TOMORROW! USE THE SMALL SEAL ON THE WARRANT.

THUS, BY BLAMING ALL "FORGETFULNESS" ON HIS MALADY, TOM WAS ACCEPTED AS THE PRINCE. THAT NIGHT . . .

IT'S TIME TO DRESS FOR THE RIVER PAG-EANT, PRINCE EDWARD.

RIVER PAG-EANT? OH . . . ER . . . YES, OF COURSE. I'D ALMOST FOR-GOTTEN!

IT WAS A WONDERFUL EXPERIENCE FOR TOM. FIRST A RIDE IN THE ROYAL BARGE ALONG THE THAMES RIVER . . .

. . . THEN A PARADE THROUGH THE LONDON STREETS TO THE GUILDHALL. . .

FOR THE FINAL EVENT. . . A HUGE BANQUET.

BUT AS TOM ATE AND MADE MERRY, ONE THOUGHT REMAINED IN THE BACK OF HIS MIND . . .

ALL THIS IS MARVELOUS. . . BUT I WONDER WHERE THE **REAL** PRINCE IS NOW. . .

IF TOM HAD LOOKED JUST OUTSIDE THE GUILDHALL, HE WOULD HAVE HAD HIS ANSWER.

HAW HAW! LISTEN TO THE YOUNG MADMAN RAVE!

SHHH! DON'T OFFEND HIS ROYAL HIGHNESS!

LET ME THROUGH! I TELL YOU I'M THE PRINCE OF WALES!

SUDDENLY A TALL MAN PUSHED HIS WAY THROUGH THE CROWD. . .

WHY DON'T YOU STOP TAUNTING HIM? LEAVE THE BOY ALONE!

WHO IS THIS SWAGGERING FOOL?

HAW HAW! ANOTHER PRINCE IN DISGUISE!

TOUCH THIS BOY... *AND YOU FORFEIT YOUR LIFE!* I, MILES HENDON, PROMISE THAT!

LOOK WHAT HE'S DONE TO PETER. LET'S KILL THE DOG!

KILL HIM!

KILL HIM!

STRAIGHT TO THE GUILDHALL SPED THE TROOPS.

COME, YOUNGSTER... LET'S GO!

AS THE CROWD PRESSED CLOSER, A TROOP OF HORSEMEN APPEARED.

OUT OF THE WAY! MAKE WAY FOR THE KING'S MESSENGER!

WATCH OUT! WE'LL BE TRAMPLED!

MEANWHILE, EDWARD RACED THROUGH THE LONDON STREETS WITH HIS NEW FRIEND.

THE KING IS DEAD!

YOUR FATHER? OF COURSE, I ALMOST FORGOT THAT YOU'RE PRINCE EDWARD, NOW KING EDWARD!

WHAT?... MY FATHER DEAD? HOW HORRIBLE.

POOR BOY! HIS SMALL HEADPIECE IS CRACKED ... BUT I WILL PROTECT HIM FROM THOSE WHO TAUNT HIM BECAUSE OF HIS MADNESS!

WE'RE NOT FAR FROM THE INN AT WHICH I'M STOPPING! I'LL TAKE YOU THERE...

BUT AS THEY APPROACHED THE INN ...

SO YOU'VE COME AT LAST!

JOHN CANTY!

YOU'RE NOT GOING TO ESCAPE THIS TIME. MAYBE POUNDING YOUR BONES TO A PUDDING WILL TEACH YOU A LESSON.

NOT SO FAST, MY FRIEND. WHO IS THIS BOY TO YOU?

WHO? THIS YOUNG SCOUNDREL IS MY SON!

THAT'S A LIE! DON'T LET HIM TAKE ME!

I BELIEVE YOU MY BOY! YOU'RE STAYING WITH ME!

WE'LL SEE ABOUT THAT!

TOUCH HIM, MY SCURVY FRIEND.. AND I'LL RUN YOU THROUGH!

THIS LAD IS UNDER MY PROTECTION. DO YOU THINK I WOULD PERMIT HIM TO FALL INTO YOUR LOWLY HANDS? GET OUT... AND BE QUICK ABOUT IT!

REMEMBER... UH, KING, I HAVE PLEDGED MYSELF TO PROTECT YOU. WHEN I'M ABOUT, YOU NEEDN'T FEAR RUFFIANS LIKE THAT ONE!

THANK YOU! YOU SHALL BE DULY REWARDED WHEN I MOUNT MY THRONE!

AS SOON AS THEY ENTERED MILE'S APARTMENT.

WELL... LOOK HOW THE LITTLE BEGGAR MAKES HIMSELF AT HOME! ONE MIGHT ALMOST BELIEVE HE *IS* A KING!

I'M TERRIBLY TIRED. CALL ME WHEN A TABLE IS SPREAD!

HE'S SHIVERING IN HIS SLEEP. I'LL COVER HIM WITH MY COAT.

EDWARD WAS ROUSED BY THE SLAMMING OF THE DOOR.

I'VE BROUGHT YOUR FOOD, SIR!

VERY GOOD, SET IT DOWN ON THE TABLE!

WHILE TOM CANTY SAT IN THE PALACE DISCHARGING HIS KINGLY DUTIES. . .

LET THIS WOMAN GO. THERE IS TOO LITTLE EVIDENCE AGAINST HER.

EDWARD THE REAL KING WALKED ALONG THE LONDON BRIDGE . . . SUPPOSEDLY TO MEET MILES HENDON.

I SHALL CHASTISE HENDON FOR HIS INSOLENCE. IS IT MUCH FURTHER?

JUST A BIT.

FINALLY . . .

HERE WE ARE NOW!

HERE?

YOUR PROTECTOR ISN'T GOING TO JOIN YOU TODAY!

WHY, WHO ARE YOU? WHAT KNAVERY IS THIS?

AND NOW, YOU LITTLE SCOUNDREL, GET IN THAT BARN AND STAY THERE UNTIL YOU FEEL READY TO GO BEGGING FOR ME AGAIN!

COME NOW. . . DON'T TELL ME THAT YOU DON'T RECOGNIZE YOUR OWN FATHER!

JOHN CANTY!

MEANWHILE, MILES HENDON CONDUCTED A FRUITLESS SEARCH FOR THE MISSING BOY.

THAT RASCALLY KNAVE WHO CALLED HIMSELF THE LAD'S FATHER MUST HAVE GOTTEN HIM!

THERE IS ONE HOPE ... THAT THE BOY WILL ESCAPE FROM HIS CAPTORS AND GO STRAIGHT TO HENDON HALL, AND THAT'S WHERE I'M GOING.

BUT FRIGHTENED AND HOPELESS, THE KING LAY IN AN OLD BARN UNTILL HE FELL INTO A TROUBLED SLEEP.

WHEN HE AWOKE THAT NIGHT, HE SAW A STRANGE SIGHT ... THE GATHERING OF A GANG OF THIEVES

WHAT'S WRONG?

OH, I'M A POOR BOY, SUFFERING FROM HUNGER. A PENNY, KIND SIR, A PENNY, PLEASE.

POOR BOY! YOU SHALL HAVE THREE! . . . AND YOU, SIR, HELP ME GET YOUR BROTHER INTO MY HOUSE!

HE'S NOT MY BROTHER!

HE'S A BEGGAR AND A THIEF! IF YOU LOOK, YOU'LL SEE THAT HE'S PICKED YOUR POCKET WHILE YOU BENT OVER HIM! AND ONE BLOW WITH YOUR STAFF WILL CURE HIS AFFLICTION!

AND NOW, I'D BETTER GET AWAY FROM HERE. THAT ENTIRE BAND WILL BE AFTER ME SOON.

ALL THAT DAY THE KING WANDERED THROUGH THE FARMLANDS . . .

JUST AFTER NIGHTFALL, HE ENTERED DENSE WOODS . . .

HOW LONELY IT IS HERE AND WHAT FUNNY SOUNDS! I HOPE I CAN FIND SOME SHELTER FOR THE NIGHT!

...HEN . . .

A LIGHTED CABIN WHAT LUCK!

ENTER AND WELCOME! MANY HAVE SOUGHT SANCTUARY HERE AND BEEN TURNED AWAY AS UNWORTHY . . . . BUT A KING WHO CASTS OFF HIS CROWN AND FINE CLOTHES TO DRESS IN HUMBLE RAGS IS INDEED WELCOME!

IT'S THE HOME OF A - HOLY HERMIT. HOW FORTUNATE!

I'M THE KING OF ENGLAND! WHO ARE YOU?

WHO ARE YOU?

...I THINK THE [LA]DY IS INSIDE. COME [W]ITH ME...

SWIFTLY MILES UNTIED THE PAUPER-KING AND HELPED HIM DON THE SUIT HE HAD BOUGHT FOR HIM ON LONDON BRIDGE... THE PAIR WASTED NO TIME HURRYING AWAY FROM THE MAD HERMIT... AT A NEARBY VILLAGE, MILES PURCHASED DONKEYS, AND IN A SHORT WHILE HE AND HIS FRIEND WERE ON THEIR WAY TO HENDON HALL.

[A]FTER HOURS OF WINDING [TH]ROUGH COUNTRY [R]OADS...

HERE WE ARE AT HENDON HALL!

TO THINK, THAT IN A MOMENT, I'LL SEE MY BELOVED EDITH! I'LL EVEN BE GLAD TO SEE MY BROTHER, HUGH, AGAIN.

I WASN'T THINKING OF HIM... I MEANT IT'S STRANGE THAT SOLDIERS HAVEN'T BEEN SENT OUT TO SEARCH FOR ME.

POOR LAD... HIS KINGLY DELUSIONS HAVEN'T LEFT HIM YET.

I'VE WORKED OUT A PLAN. I'VE WRITTEN A NOTE TELLING MY STORY IN THREE LANGUAGES. TOMORROW, YOU'LL DELIVER IT TO MY UNCLE LORD HERFORD.

AS YOU COMMAND, SIRE!

AT THAT MOMENT...

PLEASE, SIR!

EDITH... MY BELOVED—

THEN YOU STILL PRE-TEND THAT YOU DON'T KNOW ME?

I'M SORRY, SIR... BUT I DON'T!

I COME BECAUSE I FEEL SORRY FOR YOU. YOU LOOK ENOUGH LIKE MILES TO GIVE MY HUSBAND TROUBLE AND HE'LL KILL YOU. FLEE AT ONCE!

THAT'S NOT TRUE! YOU DIDN'T COME OUT OF PITY; YOU CAME BECAUSE YOU LOVE ME. I CAN'T FLEE, DON'T YOU UNDERSTAND?

ALMOST DAILY, ANDREW RETURNED PRETENDING TO COME TO INSULT MILES, BUT ACTUALLY COMING TO BRING HIM NEWS, ENCOURAGEMENT, AND FOOD.

EDITH MARRIED HUGH ONLY AFTER ALL HOPE OF YOUR BEING ALIVE HAD VANISHED. SHE ISN'T HAPPY. MILES, SHE STILL LOVES YOU!

HE THREATENED US WITH DEATH IF WE ADMITTED WE KNEW YOU! HE'S COME UP IN THE WORLD, THAT KNAVE! IN A FEW DAYS, HE'S ATTENDING THE CORONATION HOPING TO GAIN THE FAVOR OF THE NEW KING.

WHAT?... *THE CORONATION!*

MILES, DID YOU HEAR? THEY'RE CROWNING SOMEONE ELSE! WE'VE GOT TO GET TO WESTMINISTER AND STOP THEM!

MY TRIAL COMES UP TOMORROW, SIRE! WE'LL GET THERE IN TIME!

NEXT DAY, AT THE TRIAL...

I SENTENCE YOU TO TWO DAYS IN THE PILLORY. THE BOY MAY GO FREE; THOUGH IN TRUTH, HE DESERVES THE SAME SENTENCE FOR BEING IN SUCH BAD COMPANY!

WHEN EDWARD HEARD SENTENCE PASSED ON HIS FRIEND...

HOW DARE YOU DO THIS TO HIM! SET HIM FREE! I COMMAND YOU!

IN A FEW MINUTES, THE CELEBRATION HAD TURNED INTO A HUGE FIGHT...

MILES... MILES... WHERE ARE YOU? *WE'RE BEING SEPARATED!*

WHAT BAD LUCK! I CAN'T FIND HIM ANYWHERE!

AFTER THE FIGHT WAS OVER...

I'VE GOT TO GO TO THE CORONATION ALONE! MILES WILL SURELY REJOIN ME THERE!

AS HE RODE, SIGHTS HE HAD WITNESSED IN PRISON RETURNED TO HIM...

YOU HANG ME FOR STEALING A YARD OF CLOTH!

I SENT OUT PROTEST PAMPHLETS AGAINST AN INJUSTICE. FOR THAT THEY CUT OFF MY EARS.

THEY'LL BURN ME AT THE STAKE FOR MY RELIGIOUS BELIEFS.

WHEN I ASCEND THE THRONE, I AM GOING TO DO AWAY WITH THESE HORRIBLE LAWS. MY REIGN IS GOING TO BE ONE OF JUSTICE... NOT ONE OF CRUELTY!

MEANWHILE... THE MORNING OF THE CORONATION... TOM CANTY WOKE FEELING PLEASED AND HAPPY...

BEAUTIFUL CLOTHES, GOOD FOOD, EVERYTHING I WISH! I THINK I'M GOING TO LIKE BEING A KING!

... AND ON THE WAY TO THE CORONATION ITSELF, HIS HAPPINESS BECAME EVEN GREATER...

HERE, SIRE... THESE COINS ARE TO BE DISTRIBUTED AS LARGESSE!

YOU MEAN... YOU WANT ME TO THROW ALL THIS MONEY TO THE CROWDS?

HERE, MY SUBJECTS! THIS IS CERTAINLY GREAT FUN!

LARGESSE!

LARGESSE!

THEN SUDDENLY...

BY ALL THAT'S HOLY! *THAT WOMAN...*

AND HIS HAND WENT TO HIS MOUTH WITH THE HABITUAL GESTURE HE HAD ALWAYS MADE WHEN STARTLED.

IT'S HIM... IT'S TOM! OH, MY DARLING!

GET AWAY FROM THAT CARRIAGE, YOU OLD CRONE!

AS THE CARRIAGE MOVED ON, TOM HAD LOST HIS TASTE FOR KINGSHIP.

SIR, HAS THAT OLD BEGGAR DISTURBED YOU?

NO ... SHE HAS MERELY REMINDED ME HOW WRONG IT IS FOR ME TO BE HERE ... HERTFORD ... THAT WOMAN IS MY MOTHER!

MOMENTS LATER, THEY APPROACHED THE CORONATION PLATFORM AND HERTFORD HASTILY CONFERRED WITH THE ARCH BISHOP OF CANTERBURY.

THE MADNESS IS STRONG UPON HIM! HE CONTINUES TO BELIEVE HE IS THE CHILD OF PAUPERS! YOU HAD BETTER COMPLETE THE CEREMONY QUICKLY!

VERY WELL!

THE CEREMONY PROCEEDED HASTILY...

THEN, SUDDENLY ...

STOP! I AM THE REAL KING!

GET BACK INTO THE CROWD... YOU MAD BEGGAR!

NO, NO! HE IS THE REAL KING!

THE PRINCE AND THE PAUPER
MARK TWAIN

Mark Twain defined a classic as "a book people praise but don't read." Of all his works, the saying is most true about *The Prince and the Pauper*. A lilting blend of high adventure, low drama, and such traditional story-telling elements as mistaken identity and succession of kings, *The Prince and the Pauper* has become a cultural staple. Walt Disney made a popular version featuring Mickey Mouse, while other film-makers have borrowed the plot without acknowledgment. On stage, on television, in movies, Mark Twain's book has been in performance for most of the 100+ years since its publication. His friends' confidence in the book came from their belief that Twain could write a fine, socially acceptable book, if he only put his mind to it. "The time has come," his good friend Mary Fairbanks primly wrote him, "for your best book. I do not mean your most taking book, with the most money in it, I mean your best contribution to American literature." For all its middle-brow success, however, *The Prince*

and the Pauper* is too staid, formulaic, and pat to be Mark Twain's greatest contribution. It is, however an elegant and durable novel which is a pleasure to read.

The Author

Samuel Langhorne Clemens, who was born in Missouri in 1835, began signing the name Mark Twain to his journalism in the Virginia City, Nevada Territorial Enterprise, in February of 1863. He had followed his older brother Orion into the printing trade, first with an apprenticeship when he was teenager, and later into Orion's series of unsuccessful printshops. Harboring a secret ambition to get in on the ground-floor of South America's coca-leaf business, Sam Clemens instead lucked into an opportunity to become a Mississippi River steamboat pilot, his childhood ambition. Unfortunately, the Civil War interupted his successful four-year run on the river. After a two-week stint fighting for the Confederacy, Clemens traveled with his brother Orion to

Nevada, where President Abraham Lincoln had appointed Orion Clemens Territorial Secretary. Sam prospected for a few months, then landed his job at the West's finest newspaper, and began his career as Mark Twain, a career which soon encompassed not only print but performance, as Mark Twain became the nation's most popular comedian.

With his 1869 *Innocents Abroad*, about a personal

Critical Dissent from a Remarkable Friend

The man who first hired Sam Clemens as a reporter not only had a good eye for talent but also many amazing gifts himself. Younger than Clemens, Joseph Goodman had founded the West Coast's leading literary journal, The Golden Era, when he was in his early twenties. He then bought the Virginia City, Nevada, Territorial Enterprise. Virginia City was the original Wild West, a place where the first twenty-six graves were occupied by murdered men. As the force behind the Enterprise, Goodman was Twain's first and probably best editor, with the exception of his wife Livy.

Livy, a member of the East Coast bourgeoisie, adored *The Prince and the Pauper* for its grace and refinement; Goodman despised it for the same reasons. Commenting on the novel based on second-hand reports, he demanded of Twain, "What could have sent you groping among the driftwood of the Deluge for a topic when you would have been so much more at home in the wash of today?" Goodman became downright dyspeptic after reading the book. *The Prince and the Pauper*, he felt, "might have been written by anybody else—by a far less masterly hand, in fact. You went entirely out of your sphere. The laboriousness is apparent everywhere."

Goodman was not only one of the earliest connoisseurs of Mark Twain's talent, but also one of his most insightful critics. Twain's greatest literary strength lay in his dynamic use of American English; this novel has none. Twain also gave clear-eyed reports on American life and deftly distilled American attitudes toward life overseas; *The Prince and the Pauper* is devoid of both.

Joe Goodman turned his fine mind to other projects after selling the Territorial Enterprise. An amateur archaeologist, he invested two decades in studying the Mayan ruins in Mexico. In 1902, he published his findings, which included his discovery of the meanings of Mayan hieroglyphics, translations still used today. Twain noted of this feat, "I am lost in reverence and admiration! It is now twenty-four hours that I have been trying to cool down and contemplate with quiet blood this extraordinary spectacle of energy, industry, perseverance, pluck, analytical genius, penetration, this irruption of thunders and fiery splendors from a fair and flowery mountain that nobody had supposed was a sleeping volcano."

adventure in the Mediterranean, Mark Twain became a best-selling author. His follow-up narrative *Roughing It*, fictionalized from his experiences out West, sold as well as *Innocents*. Together with his short pieces and stage appearances, these books cemented Mark Twain's reputation as a comic realist, whose perceptions of the American scene were equally sharp and funny. Samuel Clemens, the man behind Mark Twain, had meanwhile married an heiress and, with

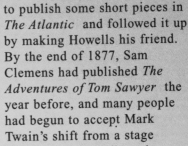

his earnings and his wife's fortune, built himself a mansion in Hartford, Connecticut. There he and his wife Livy raised several children.

Livy was also his literary director, and she helped Sam coordinate his 1870s crusade to gain Mark Twain critical acceptance. *The Atlantic Monthly* and its young editor William Dean Howells, perhaps the most influential voices in American letters, were partial to Mark Twain. Sam first campaigned

to publish some short pieces in *The Atlantic* and followed it up by making Howells his friend. By the end of 1877, Sam Clemens had published *The Adventures of Tom Sawyer* the year before, and many people had begun to accept Mark Twain's shift from a stage comedian who wrote into a literary artist who was also funny. Howells, now a good friend as well as a sponsor, got him a place on The Atlantic's program honoring the poet John Greenleaf Whittier on his seventieth birthday. But Mark Twain blew his chance with a vaguely offensive story no one found especially amusing. Sam Clemens thought he had dealt Mark Twain's reputation a devastating blow.

It was now vitally important for Mark Twain to write a book no one could mistake for low comedy. He had begun writing a sequel to *Tom Sawyer* and a more elegant story about a prince and pauper who exchange places.

He claimed to be writing the book "simply for the love of it—for it will appear without my name—such grave & stately work being considered by the world to be above my proper level." Because his friends advised him to write a book of "a sober character and a solid worth & a permanent value," he moved *The Prince and the Pauper* to the top of his fiction pile. Spending almost two years in Europe following the Whittier birthday fiasco, Mark Twain came back with vivid impressions of England in the sixteenth century. After composing another book of travel, *A Tramp Abroad*, he returned to his switch tale. Putting *Adventures of Huckleberry Finn* aside (into which Twain had dumped all of his drive to challenge society) he used only his most refined sensibilities in his

How Mark Twain Became His Own Publisher

Excluding an early collection of short works which never sold well, Mark Twain's first books were published by the American Publishing Company of Hartford, Connecticut. Under the direction of Elisha Bliss, the company had mastered the selling of books by subscription. When the population of the country was mostly rural or located in small towns, few people had the opportunity to visit a bookstore. Instead, book agents—usually ministers or school-teachers looking to boost their income—would visit members of their community and sell them books through a catalogue. Often these books were Bibles or gift books, but occasionally volumes of a different character appeared. For example, Bliss' American Publishing Company had sold 100,000 copies of a first-person account of a man's incarceration in and escape from a prison-camp during the Civil War. Sam Clemens knew about this when Bliss aproached him about collecting into a book the letters Mark Twain had sent home from his trip to the Mediterranean. The American Publishing Company sold over 100,000 copies of *Innocents Abroad* in three years. Bliss paid Clemens five percent of the return.

Elisha Bliss talked a good game when he agreed to split the profits on Mark Twain's future books, but he kept a false set of ledgers to explain to Clemens just what half-profits meant. Still, Mark Twain published book after book with the American Publishing Company, though he frequently tried to alter his contracts, sway the policy of the firm, or publish less lucratively elsewhere. His final book with Bliss' company was *A Tramp Abroad*; Bliss died not long before it was published. As his eleven-year association with the American Publishing Company neared its end, Clemens could look back on six books, 400,000 copies sold and royalty payments in excess

story of Prince Edward's exchange of places with Tom Canty. Twain got advice on the manuscript not only from Howells and other writer friends, but also from his two older children, now eight and ten, and the children of his friends and neighbors.

But when the book came out, he took no chances. He made sure that his friends reviewed the book with enthusiastic, but unsigned, reviews. Howells published an anonymous review in the *New York Daily Tribune*, "saying the book would "surprise those who had found nothing but drollery in Mark Twain's books, and have not perceived the artistic sense and the strain of deep earnestness underlying the humor." Other critics, almost all friends of the author, agreed that *The Prince and the Pauper* was Mark Twain's

---

of $100,000. On the other hand, Elisha Bliss' accounting sleights of hand, ineffective protection of Mark Twain's copyrights, and outright lies cost nearly as much. More importantly, during those years Mark Twain had become the brightest star in the American cultural firmament, an international figure. Elisha Bliss had done more to create that star than anyone but Sam Clemens himself.

Now free from his old publisher, Clemens decided to take advantage of what he learned from Bliss. By underwriting his own books and paying a "publisher" a percentage of the take to sell them by subscription, Clemens stood to recoup much of what he had lost by signing with Bliss. James Osgood, a Boston publisher whose firm had contracts with some of the nation's most prestigious writers, agreed to work with Clemens on Twain's new novel even though Osgood knew nothing about subscription publishing and Mark Twain's earlier fiction had never sold well. Astonishingly, Clemens allowed Osgood to pay the American Publishing Company, now run by Elisha Bliss' son, to use their network of book agents to sell *The Prince and the Pauper*. Osgood sold barely 25,000 copies, even with all the superb reviews Clemens had arranged. He did not do much better with Life on the Mississippi a year later.

Clemens terminated his business arrangment with Osgood and in 1884 established Charles L. Webster & Co. Named for his nephew-by-marriage, who was the company president, but run by Clemens, this company sold Mark Twain's books, funneling all the profits directly to the author himself. Webster & Co., did well with its first book, Huck Finn, and made a precedent-setting smash hit with its second, The Personal Memoirs of Ulysses S. Grant, but the company then floundered under Charley Webster's poor management. And, as the population moved to the cities, the book business changed and the sale of books by subscription disappeared. Mark Twain's company had trouble converting to selling through bookstores and went bankrupt in 1894.

greatest book, and at the same time an enormous departure. The book contained only sporadic humor and, though unmistakeably grounded in history, was more fantasy than realism. Sam Clemens had a more practical reason than his simple desire for literary success for enrolling his friends in promoting the book. He had underwritten the publication of the book himself, and stood to make a small fortune if the book sold as well as his books of travel had. As it turned out, the book sold only moderately well; the reading public prefered their Mark Twain to be funny. He had more success with the scandalous Huck Finn a few years later.

Sam Clemens' speculation on Mark Twain's literary success was a part of Clemens' drive to accumulate wealth. He invested in a number of inventions, most notably a mechanical typesetter, and established his own publishing firm. His investments seldom panned out, however, and by 1894, both the typesetting machine and the publishing firm had gone bust. Bankrupt, Clemens had to take Mark Twain on a 'round-the-world tour in 1895-6 to earn enough money to repay his creditors. His eldest daughter Susy died while he was on tour, and his wife Livy never recovered

from the loss. She died in 1904. Mark Twain rebounded after her death for a few years as the white-clothed philosopher—the most photographed and most quoted man in the world. In 1909 Clemens fell ill, his heart succumbing to the forty cigars he smoked each day. His youngest daughter, Jean, drowned in the tub on Christmas Eve the same year. Samuel Langhorne Clemens died on April 21, 1910.

Cast of Characters

Tom Canty
a poor boy of uncertain age
John Canty
his brutish father, a drunk and a thief
Gammer Canty
a drunken fiend, a beggar
Mother Canty
Tom's kindly mother
Nan and Bet Canty
Tom's twin sisters, fifteen, "unclean, clothed in rags, and profoundly ignorant"
Father Andrew
the priest in Tom's neighborhood who teaches Tom to read
Edward Tudor
Prince and successor to

TOMORROW HE'LL BE INSTALLED AS HEIR TO THE THRONE IN ALL DUE AND ANCIENT CEREMONY. TAKE THAT AS AN INSTANT ORDER, LORD HERTFORD!

BUT...

King Henry VIII
of England, now desperately ill
Lady Elizabeth
Edward's sister
Lady Jane Grey
his cousin
Humphrey Marlow
the Prince's whipping boy
Earl of Hertford, the Lord Chancellor
*the King's advisor, and Tom's
courtier when thought to be the
deranged Prince of Wales*
Lord St. John
another courtier
Duke of Norfolk
*the Hereditary Great Marshall,
under the King's sentence of
death for treason*
The Ruffler, Jack, Hobbs and Hugo
*John Canty's criminal
associates*
The Mad Hermit
himself
Miles Hendon
*Edward Tudor's guardian
while the prince finds himself
adrift beyond the castle walls*
Hugh Hendon
*Miles' evil brother, who has
stolen his fortune and denied
his brother's existence*
Edith Hendon
*formerly Miles' wife,
now Hugh's wife*
Blake Andrews
Miles Hendon's faithful servant

Plot

The Classic Illustrated adaptation of *The Prince and the Pauper* renders the plot with great faith. It shortens Tom Canty's experience as the King of England, particularly his service as a judge, which goes a long way toward restoring the court's belief in his sanity, and it beautifies the King's harsher experiences on the road. The realism Twain tries to inject into his story in the brutality of the thieves' treatment of one another and in the treatment of trespassers by legal authorities never quite integrates itself into the plot. The plot itself is an ancient one, and the motif of two look-alikes exchanging places in society is basically fantasy; historical realism sits awkwardly in the fairy-tale plot at the heart of *The Prince and the Pauper*.

Writers have used twins, or just look-alikes, as in the case of Tom Canty and Edward Tudor, since the beginning of literature to communicate the idea of a person divided against himself. In more political sto-

WHEN HE WAS HANDED A FINGER BOWL WITH ROSE WATER . . .

HE'S DRINKING FROM IT!

I DON'T LIKE IT. IT HAS A PRETTY FLAVOR BUT IT LACKS STRENGTH!

Making a Play
Out of the Prince

Mark Twain first conceived of *The Prince and the Pauper* as a stage play. He had made a pile of money from the loose stage adaptation of his first novel, *The Gilded Age*, co-authored with his Hartford neighbor Charles Dudley Warner, and he later told his business manager and nephew-by-marriage, Charley Webster, "If the book business interferes with the dramatic business, drop the former—for it doesn't pay salt." Though a successful play was made of *The Prince and the Pauper*, however, it paid less than salt.

Clemens had encouraged Ned House, a crippled and belea-guered friend, to dramatize the novel, but when he had not heard anything from House regarding the play, he accepted a deal from writer Abby Sage Richardson: if she could deliver child-star Elsie Leslie to play both Prince Edward and Tom Canty, then Richardson could write the adaptation. New York's theatre world was like Hollywood today. Stars and producers set the terms and made most of the money, but those few writers, directors and actors who beat the long odds landed a successful play also profited. The young Leslie had starred in The Little Prince and was in great demand. She

ries—like this one—twins can also represent a nation divided against itself. Twins have great comic value, because a confusion of identity can be easily milked for humor, as happens when Tom finds himself incapable of mastering the ritual of royal dining (see bottom of previous page). A plot with two sets of twins, and the endless confusion resulting from their misidentification has been around since ancient Greece in the form of *The Twin Menaechme*, was used by

Shakespeare, and later became the musical-comedy *The Boys from Syracuse*. This trope of twinship has also been inverted for more serious purpose when a single body houses two personalities; as in Robert Louis Stevenson's *Dr. Jekyll and Mr. Hyde*, the twins are merged into a single body, but the selves remain separate. This image can carry darker meanings, though Steve Martin and Lily Tomlin used it for comic effect in the film *All of Me*. In stories, twins can be used to agreed to appear in *The Prince and the Pauper*, and Richardson was named dramatist.

But Ned House objected. He claimed that Clemens had already commissioned him to write the adaptation. Richardson would not step aside, and the producer forced a contract which saved him from any problems House might cause. When the play opened early in the winter of 1890, two productions ran simultaneously, House's pirate version in Brooklyn, and the production with Leslie in Manhattan. A judge eventually agreed to shut down House's production, but only if the money from the other version were put in escrow until a court could decide what rights, and what money, belonged to House.

The Leslie production—charming because of the young star, but devoid of much of the drama because the Prince and the Pauper could not appear on stage at the same time—ran successfully in New York and on the road, but Mark Twain never received a penny for his role in the play.

He did get a hefty measure of joy from the short adaptation he had done himself. During Mark Twain's fall 1884 lecture tour in support of Huck Finn, his wife Livy co-ordinated a surprise production of *The Prince and the Pauper*, featuring his fourteen-year-old daughter Susy and Daisy Warner, the daughter of Twain's Gilded Age collaborator. In one family production, he himself played Miles Hendon.

signal certain themes; these stories tend to follow a time-honored formula of comic inversion, sometimes with tragic results.

Perhaps because of his own double identity, Mark Twain/Sam Clemens returned frequently to stories involving twins and twinship. He explored the comic potential of Siamese twins in an few early short pieces, and used the confusion of identity effectly throughout his work. In the 1890s, he wrote a farce concerning some Siamese twins

from Italy in a small Mississippi River town, but then converted the farce into a tragedy with the addition of another set of twins, one slave and the other free, whose identities are switched in infancy. In that novel, *Pudd'nhead Wilson*, Twain managed to integrate the rather artificial device of twins with the realistic depiction of life in a small, slave-holding Missouri town. In most of his fiction, in fact, Mark Twain attempted to yoke together the ingredients of myth and legend with a style of

writing that suggested a realistic—that is, historically accurate and true to life—narrative. This succeeded in *Huck Finn*, but in *The Prince and the Pauper* the two forms never seem to completely co-exist. Maybe that is why, in the CI adaptation of the story, so much of the harsher realism of the novel is missing.

The political subplot regarding the rightful ownership of power is likewise submerged under the more traditional plot of exchanged identities. We read the story because we want to find out how Tom and Edward will get back together again, not because we care that much whether it's Tom or Edward who actually occupies the throne of England. In that way, the book is almost like a love story between the boys: two boys meet. They discover a powerful likeness between them, which goes beyond the similarity of their physiques. Then fate separates them and they each must face great peril until they find one another again. When they do, all is right with the world and the two live happily ever after.

Mark Twain seemed to know that he had not accomplished what he intended to with the political subplot in *The Prince and the Pauper*, because in the years after the novel's publication he returned to it. In *A Connecticut Yankee in King Arthur's Court* , a modern man finds himself transported into the past, where he uses his technological superiority to accumulate power and drag the primitive culture he finds headlong into the future. The novel explores some of the same themes as *The Prince and the Pauper*: the progressiveness of history, the rightful ownership of power, the significance of education in increasing social justice. But Twain wrote his later book exclusively for adults, allowing his narrative to roam freely to whatever interested him. The traditional plot of *The Prince and the*

Pauper keeps it close to its narrative line, seldom moving away from the eventual working out of the confusion wrought be the exchange of places. This leaves Twain little room to explore subplots which might develop his historical and political themes; it also renders the novel a little simple, if not simplistic. Even with his great artistry, Mark Twain seems unable to imbue the timeless plot of *The Prince and the Pauper* with a vitality of lived life. The greatness of the book depends on the masterful working out of its venerable and mythical plot, not on any unique perspective Twain might have given the material.

Themes

There is only one major theme in *The Prince and the Pauper*, and it is the simplicity of the novel's meaning which has kept it from being ranked higher by literary scholars than it has, despite its elegant construction, excellent characterization and fine language. Modern critics prefer books with layers of meaning, and typically equate complexity with quality. Whether or not this is true, most critics have preferred the challenge of *Huck Finn*, *A Connecticut Yankee in King Arthur's Court* or *Pudd'nhead Wilson* to *The Prince and the Pauper*'s single-note theme.

The Progress of History

An avid reader of history, Sam Clemens conducted an ongoing debate with himself about whether civilizations improved with time. Did things get better—more moral, more just, more peaceful—over time? Or did periods of greater kindness simply happen at random in the string of human cruelty which dominated human history? Clemens was of course not the first person to be engaged by this question. Historians of his day regularly speculated about the nature of history and its implications for the direction of society. It was an era of enormous change: improvements to transportation and communication had completely altered not only American and European concepts of the world, but of people's experience of the world as well. It's no wonder they wanted to figure out where their society might be going.

One notable historian who influenced Mark Twain's composition of *The Prince and the Pauper* was W. E. H. Lecky. Lecky's *History of European Morals* held that society became less barbaric through each individual's experience and education. If one individual discovers the moral and social benefits of mercy, for example, those people who have received merciful treatment from him or her will likely begin to practice mercy themselves. Those who learn the costs of barbarism find ways to avoid it. Thus society improves through time, imperceptibly at first and then rapidly as more and more people begin to learn to shun barbaric behaviors.

condemned as a witch. A lawyer is branded on both cheeks, loses both his ears, and spends his life in prison for writing a pamphlet against the Lord Chancellor. The scene in which Miles Hendon is whipped is among the mildest abuses of authority depicted in the novel. Both Tom, in his unaccustomed position as judge, and Edward, in his equally unaccustomed experi-

In order to communicate this idea in *The Prince and the Pauper*—and to explore its truth—Mark Twain includes many examples of institutional—and personal—barbarism. The cruelty of John and Gammer Canty to Tom or the rough treatment he receives from the guard outside the castle show people at their worst, but Twain was less interested in an individual's bad behavior than in abuses of governmental authority. The novel includes several stories told by victims of law. Yokel, formerly a prosperous farmer, ends up a slave after his mother, a nurse, is

ence with the real world, learn of the horrific nature of authority in sixteenth- century England and vow to make changes.

Clemens wrote to his friend and fellow author William Dean Howells while he was in the midst of composing his novel, "My idea is to afford a realizing sense of the exceeding severity of the laws of that day by inflicting some of their penalties upon the king himself & allowing him a chance to see the rest of them applied to others—all of which is to account for certain mildnesses which distinguished Edward VI's reign from those that preceded & followed it." But the novel itself says nothing about the

AS HE RODE, SIGHTS HE HAD WITNESSED IN PRISON RETURNED TO HIM...

YOU HANG ME FOR STEALING A YARD OF CLOTH!

I SENT OUT PROTEST PAMPHLETS AGAINST AN INJUSTICE. FOR THAT THEY CUT OFF MY EARS.

THEY'LL BURN ME AT THE STAKE FOR MY RELIGIOUS BELIEFS.

years after Edward VI left the throne, during which his half-sister Bloody Mary presided over a brief period of nearly random violence, or even the subsequent reign of Elizabeth I, which had its own share of torture and oppression of political dissenters. *The Prince and the Pauper* opens the question of whether or not society progresses toward greater kindness, but it does not fully answer it. Discussing the famed Blue-Laws of Connecticut, which even in Mark Twain's day had the reputation of severity, Twain notes, "There has never been a time—under the Blue-Laws or any other—when above FOUR-TEEN crime were punishable by death in Connecticut. But in England, within the memory of men who are still hale in body and mind, TWO HUNDRED AND TWENTY-THREE crimes were punishable by death. These facts are worth know-ing—and worth thinking about, too." This observation implies a promise that society will become even more just as time goes by, but *The Prince and the Pauper* has to fudge the truth to demonstrate this overriding idea.

Image and Identity

The progressiveness of history is not the novel's only theme, though it is unquestionably its most important. Any story which includes characters who switch positions also must explore the themes of image and identity. Who is Tom Canty? Who is Edward Tudor? Where does the authority of royalty lie? Is it in the image of the king or in his identity? Tom Canty appears to have something innately royal about him, since the poverty-stricken inhabitants of Offal Court regard him as "a most gifted and extraordinary creature. Full grown people

TOM'S FRIENDS WERE FIRST AMUSED, THEN AWED. TOM EVEN ORGANIZED A ROYAL COURT.

I DUB YOU FIRST LORD OF THE ROYAL FOOTWEAR. IT WOULD BE YOUR DUTY TO PUT ON MY SHOES, IF I HAD SHOES.

OH, THANK YOU, PRINCE TOM!

brought their perplexities to Tom for solution, and were often astonished at the wit and wisdom of his decisions." Everyone—except his family—sees him as a better person, despite his poverty and disadvantages. Twain seems to argue that this refinement of character came with Tom Canty from the womb, but Twain makes it clear that Tom only begins to accept the duties of royalty after he has put on the trappings of royalty. "Tom's reading and dreaming about princely life wrought such a strong effect upon him that he began to act the prince, unconsciously. His speech and manners became curiously ceremonious and courtly."

Throughout the book, there is a tension between appearance and reality. For example, Hugh Hendon appears to be the rightful inheritor of his father's lands, but Miles is in fact. In many ways, Twain does a better job with this less important theme than he does with his more developed one about history, because he does not falsify his story in order to make his point.

...BUT, SIRE, HAVE YOU FORGOTTEN THE DUKE OF NORFOLK, WHO IS TO PERFORM THE CEREMONY, IS YOUR POLITICAL PRISONER? YOU HAD HIM LOCKED IN THE TOWER. HE IS TO DIE AT SUNRISE!

Power When it comes to power, *The Prince and the Pauper* is the rawest fictional exploration Mark Twain wrote. All the relationships in the book, with the exception of that between Tom and Edward, are about power. There are constant debates and disagreements about who gets to command whom, who must stand in another's presence, who must address whom deferentially. It is especially interesting that these power relationships always seem to rely on physical force. Argument about authority ends when one party chains, brands, stabs, kicks, burns or whips another. Although it is a political truism that physical authority is the ultimate expression of power—that is, that the government is powerful because it can lock you up if you don't pay your taxes—it is unusual to regard force as the essence of power. Mark Twain introduces a single exception into this rule, in the relationship between *The Prince and the Pauper*, in which power seems nearly irrelevant. It is possible that he does this because Tom and Edward are meant to be not only look-alikes, but the same, a single entity some how; power doesn't matter if there aren't at least two people to dispute it.

•Mark Twain thoroughly researched the age about in which *The Prince and the Pauper* takes place, and critics of his day praised his rendering of the world of King Edward VI. Has his portrait of the age held up? Does it seem less true now than it did a century ago? Have modern readers found flaws that slipped by earlier generations? If the picture of the age does seem false, how does that falseness alter your interpretation of the book?

•The sixteenth century in England was a period of tremendous religious upheaval. How does this change show itself in *The Prince and the Pauper*?

•What point does Mark Twain have, other than humor, in Tom Canty's trouble in learning how to be a prince?

•In many ways, Miles Hendon is the hero of this novel. He's the one who saves the king; he's the one whose gallantry and courage moves the story along; it is his betrayal by his brother which draws more sympathy that Edward's absence from the throne. Despite all this, the book is not about Miles Hendon. Why? How does the book focus on the prince even though he does not play much of a role in the most exciting and dynamic action?

•In what sense are the Prince and the Pauper twins? What meaning does their twinship have for the book?

•Sam Clemens, as the backer of *The Prince and the Pauper*, decided to publish the novel under his trade-name Mark Twain, even though he doubted that most of Twain's audience would be able to accept a serious book from their favorite humorist. Publishing as Mark Twain was a commercial decision. Can you detect other elements in the novel which seem more calculated to sell the book than to improve it?

• Sam Clemens's father died when the writer was just eleven years old. Mark Twain's characters are frequently fatherless, and what fathers do appear are often drunk and brutal, like Tom

. . . TOM HAD BEEN MADE TO BEG . . .

WHAT . . . YOU'VE BEGGED ONLY A SINGLE PENNY TODAY! TAKE THIS, YOU LAZY FOOL!

Canty, or sickly and emotionally absent, like Henry VIII. What connection can you make between the death of John Clemens and the role his son assigned to fathers in *The Prince and the Pauper*?

• Twain's daughters, Susy and Clara Clemens, regarded *The Prince and the Pauper* as their father's best work; their mother Livy agreed. Is there something about the book itself that would make them prize it more than *Adventures of Huckleberry Finn*, which most modern readers rank far above *The Prince and the Pauper*?

• What does the novel seem to say about the problem of birth vs. training? Are Tom and Edward more merciful than almost everyone else in their worlds because they were born that way or because

THEN FROM THIS DAY THE KING'S LAW SHALL BE ONE OF MERCY. . . NOT BLOOD! GO TO THE TOWER AND TELL THEM THAT THE DUKE OF NORFOLK SHALL NOT DIE!

their world taught them to be?